All paws on deck!

This book belongs to

....

....

This edition published by Parragon Books Ltd in 2016

Parragon Books Ltd
Chartist House
15–17 Trim Street
Bath BA1 1HA, UK
www.parragon.com

ISBN 978-1-8453-5608-8

Printed in Poland

ANNUAL 2017

Bath • New York • Cologne • Melbourne • Delhi
Hong Kong • Shenzhen • Singapore

Contents

PAW Patrol, let's roll!

Meet the heroic pups of PAW Patrol. They're always ready to race to the rescue. Whenever there's trouble, just yelp for help! Team leader Ryder picks the perfect pup for every emergency.

Rocky

Skye

Chase

Rubble

Marshall

Zuma

Everest

Ryder

Chase
on the case

Pup name: Chase
Breed: German shepherd
Skills: Tracking, traffic control
Chase is ... allergic to cats and feathers.

My nose knows!

1 Chase has lots of useful gadgets in his Pup Pack.
Circle the object that belongs to him.

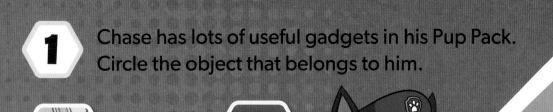

2

Check your answers on page 68.

What do you love
most about this pup?
Pick one of the words below,
and then copy it into the space.

I love Chase because he is

....

clever   loyal   adventurous

3 Bring brave Chase to life
with your brightest crayons
or colouring pencils. Use
the paw prints to help you
pick the right shades.

My oh Marshall!

Pup name: Marshall
Breed: Dalmatian
Skills: Fire-fighting, ladder rescues
Marshall is ... quite clumsy!

To the ruff-ruff rescue!

1 Dalmatian Marshall has special markings. Trace over the word that describes his PAWsome coat.

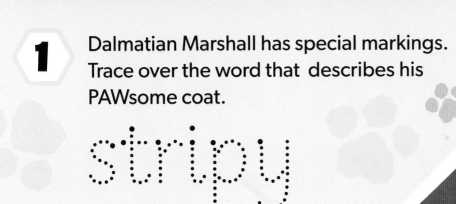

stripy

spotty

2 What do you love most about this pup? Pick one of the words below, and then copy it into the space.

I love Marshall because he is

....

funny

friendly

brave

3 Uh-oh! Marshall's been sleepwalking again. Can you help him find his way back to the Lookout?

START

FINISH

Check your answers on page 68.

Rubble
on the double

Pup name: Rubble
Breed: Bulldog
Skills: Building, digging
Rubble is ... fond of warm baths!

I can dig it!

1 Uh-oh! Rubble's helmet has fallen off.
Draw a line to match him up with it again.

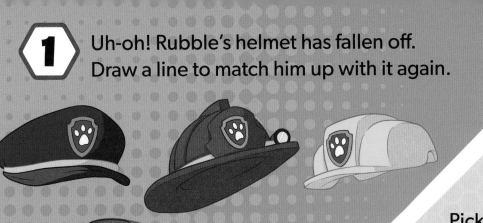

2

What do you love
most about this pup?
Pick one of the words below,
and then copy it into the space.

I love Rubble because he is

....

 tough

 kind

strong

3 Rubble has been busy digging! Help him count the bones he has
dug up, and then draw some yummy pup treats in his bowl.

Rubble has counted .... **bones.**

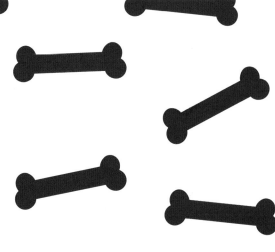

Check your answers on page 68.

Rocky to the rescue

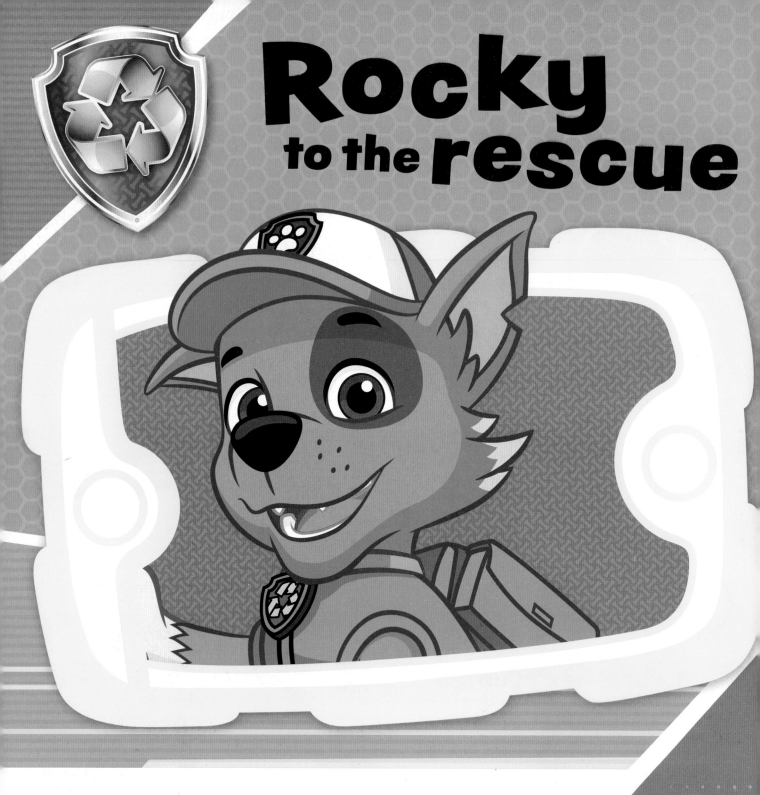

Pup name: Rocky
Breed: Mixed breed
Skills: Recycling, solving problems
Rocky is ... sometimes a scruffy pup!

Green means GO!

1 Rocky drives a big, green recycling truck. Can you spot his truck in the close-ups below? Circle the one that belongs to him.

2

What do you love most about this pup? Pick one of the words below, and then copy it into the space.

I love Rocky because he is

....

honest

caring

inventive

3 There are five differences between these two pictures of Rocky. Can you circle them all?

Check your answers on page 68.

15

Let's fly, Skye!

Pup name: Skye
Breed: Cockapoo
Skills: Flying, memorizing facts
Skye is ... great at playing Pup Pup Boogie!

This pup's gotta fly!

1 'S' is for Skye! Look at the pictures, and then circle the objects that begin with the letter 'S'.

2 What do you love most about this pup? Pick one of the words below, and then copy it into the space.

I love Skye because she is

....

🐾 **loyal**   🐾 **smiley**   🐾 **daring**

3 Look at the trail from Skye's jet pack – the little puffs of smoke are making a shape in the sky! Can you see what it is? Join the dots to find out.

3

2   4

1   5

10   6

8

9   7

Check your answers on page 68.

Dive in with Zuma

Pup name: Zuma
Breed: Chocolate Labrador
Skills: Water rescues, scuba diving
Zuma is ... always laughing and joking!

Ready, set get Wet!

1 Zuma uses his Pup Pack gadgets to be a brilliant rescue dog! Draw a tick next to his extra-special splash-tastic skill.

A. Flying in the sky.

B. Swimming underwater.

C. Digging big holes.

D. Seeing in the dark.

2 What do you love most about this pup? Pick one of the words below, and then copy it into the space.

I love Zuma because he is

....

 **energetic**  **happy**  **funny**

3 Zuma loves to laugh. Check out his favourite doggy jokes.

What do you call a doggy magician? *Labracadabrador!*

What is the PAW Patrol's favourite pizza flavour? *Pup-peroni!*

How did the small dog feel when he saw a ghost? *Terrier-fied!*

Check your answer on page 68.

19

Absolutely Everest

Pup name: Everest
Breed: Husky
Skills: Mountain rescue, clearing forest trails
Everest is ... a fan of belly-bogganing.

Ice or snow, I'm ready to go!

1 One of these objects would not be very useful in Everest's snowy mountains. Can you circle it?

Life Buoy

Snowboard

2 What do you love most about this pup? Pick one of the words below, and then copy it into the space.

I love Everest because she is

....

helpful   **fearless**   **bright**

Check your answers on page 68.

3 How well do you know the newest member of the PAW Patrol? Try this quiz to find out!

A Everest loves the snow.
YES
NO

B Everest drives a sledge.
YES
NO

C Everest lives on Seal Island.
YES
NO

In the spotlight

Oh, no! All the lights have gone out on Main Street.
Chase is using his searchlight to help. Who can he see in its beam?

Check your answers on page 68.

Time for a treat

Each member of the PAW Patrol has their own special bowl – perfect for special pup treats! Draw lines to match each pup to their bowl.

One pup's bowl is missing. Point to the odd pup out.

Check your answers on page 68.

Recall to action

The PAW Patrol has just completed another successful mission in Adventure Bay. Look at this picture for 30 seconds. When you've finished, cover the bottom half of these pages with some paper and try to answer the questions. You can write your answers on the piece of paper.

1. Which pup is licking Ryder's cheek?

2. Are Skye's goggles blue or pink?

3. Which pup is wearing a red Pup Pack?

4. What is Zuma carrying in his mouth?

5. Is Everest next to Chase or next to Skye?

6. Is Rubble wearing his yellow helmet?

How many questions did you answer? Give yourself a **PAW Patrol** pat on the back!

Check your answers on page 68.

Pup, pup and away!

It was the day of the Adventure Bay Balloon Race. Chase and Rubble were helping Mayor Goodway prepare for the big day. Ryder had agreed to be her co-pilot.

"Why did I ever agree to a balloon race?" she said. "I have to get over my fear of heights."

"I'll be there to help you," said Ryder. "Ready to unroll the balloon, pups?"

"We're ready!" barked Rubble.

The balloon was so dusty that poor Chase began to sneeze.

"Uh-oh!" he said. "It's got a ... a ... **ATISHOO!** ... a hole. A ripped balloon can't hold air!"

Mayor Goodway groaned. "Mayor Humdinger will win again!"

Ryder reached for his PupPad.

"We'll get this balloon ready for the race," he smiled.

"No job is too big, no pup is too small."

The PAW Patrol pups assembled at the Lookout.
"Ready for action, Ryder, sir!" Chase barked.
Ryder explained the problem with Mayor Goodway's torn balloon.
"Rocky, can you find something in your recycling truck that we can use to patch it up?" he asked.
"Don't lose it, reuse it!" nodded Rocky.

"The hot air that makes the balloon rise comes from a gas flame," continued Ryder. "Marshall, I'll need you to make sure the heater is safe."
"I'm all **fired up!**" Marshall exclaimed.

The PAW Patrol raced back to the town square. Rocky inspected the tear in the balloon. "I've got the perfect patch in my truck," he said, running off to fetch it.

"And how are the gas tanks?" Ryder asked Marshall.

The pup quickly sniffed the tanks.

"I don't smell any gas leaks," he replied.

Rocky glued a piece of Zuma's old kitesurfing canopy over the tear.

"Good work!" Ryder exclaimed. "That patch is a perfect fit!"

He turned a lever and the balloon slowly filled with hot air. The mayor climbed in. Other balloons were gathering on the horizon, too. The race was about to begin.

"Time to get over my fear of heights!" cried the mayor. "I've got to win!"

She pumped her fist, but as she did so, she accidentally hit the lever controlling the heater. The heater flipped all the way open, sending the balloon **soaring** upwards!

Marshall chased after the balloon. He tried to stop it flying away by grabbing onto the rope with his teeth, but it was too heavy. The balloon tugged the pup into the air.

Suddenly, the rope slid out of Marshall's mouth and he fell to the ground. Luckily Ryder was on hand to catch him.

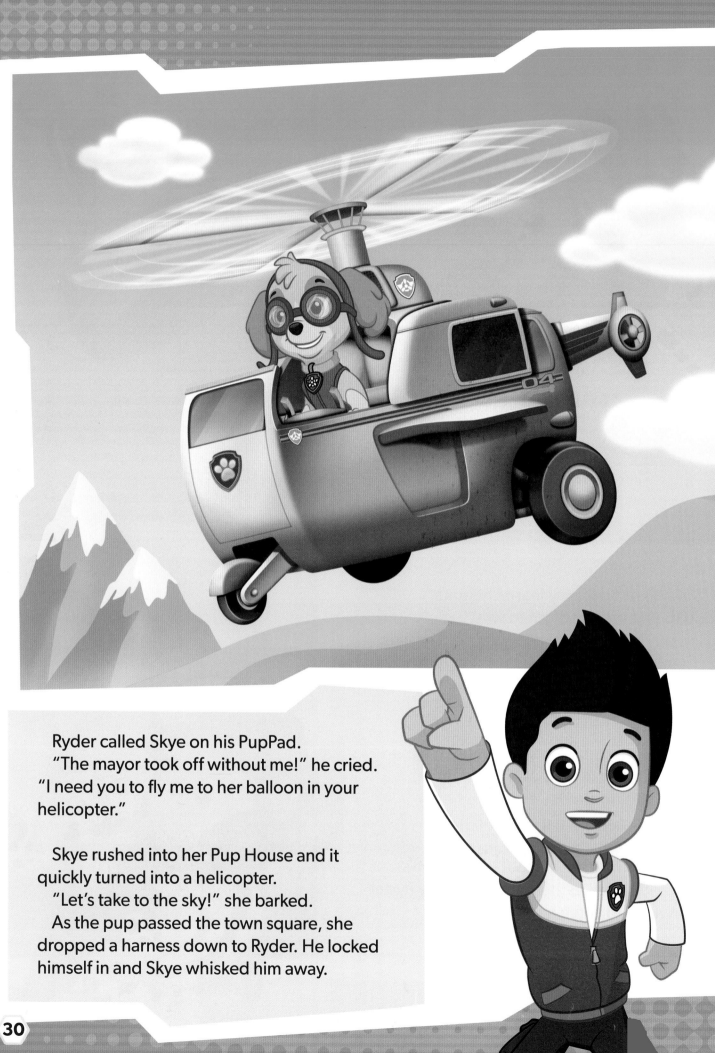

Ryder called Skye on his PupPad.
"The mayor took off without me!" he cried.
"I need you to fly me to her balloon in your helicopter."

Skye rushed into her Pup House and it quickly turned into a helicopter.
"Let's take to the sky!" she barked.
As the pup passed the town square, she dropped a harness down to Ryder. He locked himself in and Skye whisked him away.

Skye **zoomed** off after the mayor. She was flying towards Seal Island. "I'll swing you over to the balloon," she called to Ryder.

Skye knew she had to be quick – the balloon was flying dangerously low. Right now it was on a collision course with the Island's lighthouse!

Skye hovered beside the balloon, and then skilfully swung Ryder up towards the basket. As soon as he had climbed in, Ryder gave the balloon a **burst** of hot air, sending it soaring safely over the lighthouse.

"Made it, Skye!" Ryder reported.

"All right, Mayor Goodway," said Ryder, "are you ready to win this race?"

Mayor Goodway gave him a thumbs-up. With Ryder at the controls, they soon caught up with the other balloons.

Mayor Humdinger was in the lead. When he saw Ryder and Mayor Goodway, he pressed on even faster.

"I've never lost a race and I'm not starting now!" he shouted.

With a rush of hot air Ryder and Mayor Goodway's balloon suddenly **whooshed** past Mayor Humdinger. Up ahead they saw Jake's Mountain. The finish line was on the other side!

"The winds are stronger up high," Ryder said. "We'll have a better chance of winning if we go up."

He carefully rode the winds over Jake's Mountain, but Mayor Humdinger did the same. He was in the lead again.

The balloons **swooped** down towards the finish line. Humdinger was still in first place, but just at the last second, Mayor Goodway and Ryder dropped ahead of him. They were the winners!

Mayor Humdinger handed the trophy to Mayor Goodway.
"This belongs to Ryder and the PAW Patrol," she decided, passing it on to Ryder.
"Thanks!" Ryder smiled. "Whenever you need a hand, just yelp for help!"

THE END

Picture paw-cards

The PAW Patrol team have been taking a well-earned holiday. Read each message, and then draw lines to match the messages to the correct postcard pictures.

1

I've been busy snowboarding, building snowmen and riding in a cable car.
See you soon,
Chase

2

This holiday is PAWsome! I've been fishing every day and I've even visited the lighthouse.
Rubble

3

Hey there,
I've been surfing, sunbathing and building sandcastles!
It's a ruff-ruff life!
Love Marshall

4

I'm having such fun sliding and swinging! This is a great place to play frisbee.
From Zuma

A

B

C

D

Check your answers on page 68.

Skye's S.O.S.

Someone's in trouble! Can you read out Skye's S.O.S. message? Each time you see a picture, say the right word instead and then colour it in.

Calling

It's . This is an S.O.S. Call the PAW Patrol

on your . I was out in my  when

I saw a hot air balloon caught on the bridge.

I could see that someone was trapped

in the basket of the balloon. Please ask

to stop the traffic going over the bridge

so that can get them down with his ladder.

 should wait on the water under the bridge,

just in case. PAW Patrol, let's roll!

Check your answers on page 68.

Paw-print cupcakes

Hungry helpers always deserve a treat. These paw-print cupcakes are really easy to make and they taste PAWsome! This recipe makes 12 yummy cakes – plenty to share with all of your team!

YOU WILL NEED:

For the cupcakes:

- 150g lightly salted butter, softened
- 150g caster sugar
- 3 eggs
- 125g self-raising flour
- 25g cocoa powder
- 2 teaspoons vanilla extract
- 1 tablespoon milk

For the chocolate buttercream:

- 100g unsalted butter, softened
- 150g icing sugar
- 25g cocoa powder
- 2 tablespoons hot water
- 2 teaspoons vanilla extract
- a handful of large and small white chocolate buttons

1

To make the cupcakes, preheat the oven to 180°C/350°F/Gas Mark 4. Line a 12-section bun tray with paper cupcake cases. Put all of the ingredients in a mixing bowl and beat with a wooden spoon or electric mixer until the mixture is smooth and creamy.

Ovens are hot. Ask a grown-up to help you with this recipe.

2

Divide the mixture between the cases. Bake in the preheated oven for 20–25 minutes, or until firm to the touch. Transfer to wire racks to cool.

Preparation time: 10 minutes, plus cooling

 Cooking time: 20–25 minutes

 Decoration time: 10 minutes

3

To make the buttercream, put the butter in a mixing bowl and beat with a wooden spoon or electric mixer to soften. Add the icing sugar and beat well until smooth and creamy. Blend the cocoa powder with the hot water to make a paste and add to the buttercream with the vanilla. Beat until smooth and creamy.

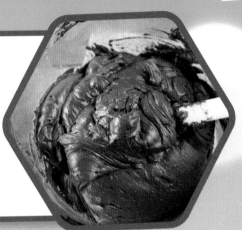

4

Using a palette knife, spread the cupcakes with the buttercream in a smooth layer.

5

Now it's time to add the paw prints! Press one large white chocolate button into each cupcake to make the main paw pad, and then add three or four small ones above it for the toes.

Choppy chums

If someone gets stuck in choppy waters, they can count on Zuma and Ryder to dive in and save the day!

Use a pencil to trace over the lines in the grid on the opposite page. You can use this picture as a guide.

Now colour in your picture!

Check your answer on page 69.

Which vehicle does Zuma drive?
Put a tick in the correct box.

1 Jet ski

2 Hovercraft

3 Fire engine

Yelp for help!

It's a busy day at the Lookout today and Ryder needs your help! Choose the perfect PAW Patrol member to send out to the rescue.

Draw a line to match each emergency with the correct pup.

1 There's a fire at City Hall!

2 A kitty is stuck on the top of a bridge, you'll need to fly up to reach her.

3 Rocks are blocking the train track. You'll need a digger to scoop them.

4 It has been snowing in town and the snow is blocking the pavements.

5 A broken tricycle needs to be patched up and rebuilt.

A

B

C

D

E

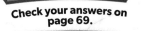
Check your answers on page 69.

40

Dot-to-spot

Marshall is an amazing fire pup. He can fight any fire with his double spray hose! Join the dots to complete the picture, and then colour him in using bright-red crayons or pencils.

I'm fired up!

PAW Patrol is on a roll!

PAW PATROL

Ready, steady, Rocky!

Help Rocky complete these picture patterns.
Point to the object that comes next in each row,
and then write the correct letter in the circle.

1 🐾 🐾 🦴 🐾 ◯

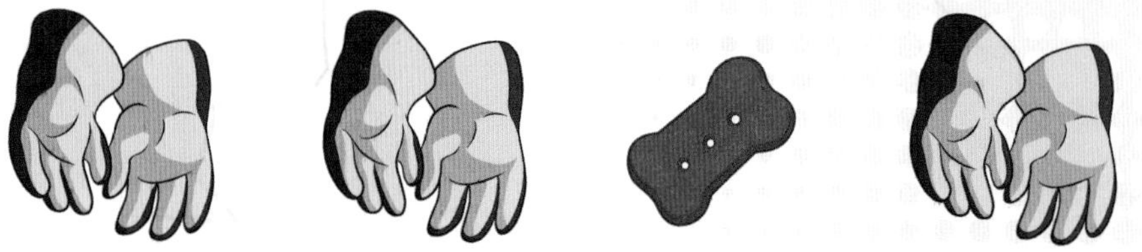

2 🥣 🦴 🥣 🦴 ◯

3 🧢 🧢 🐾 🧢 ◯

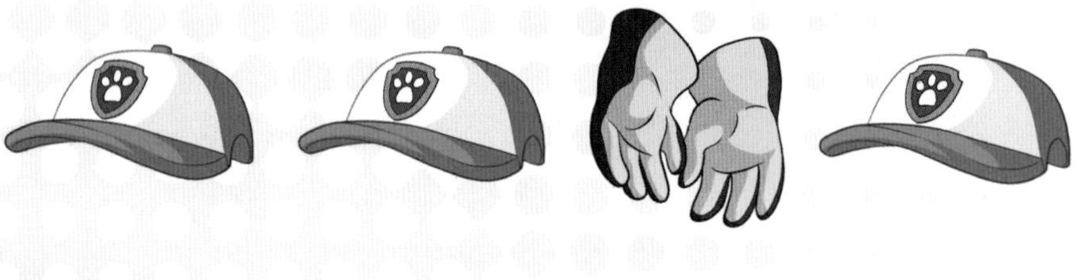

A 🐾   **B** 🧢   **C** 🦴   **D** 🥣

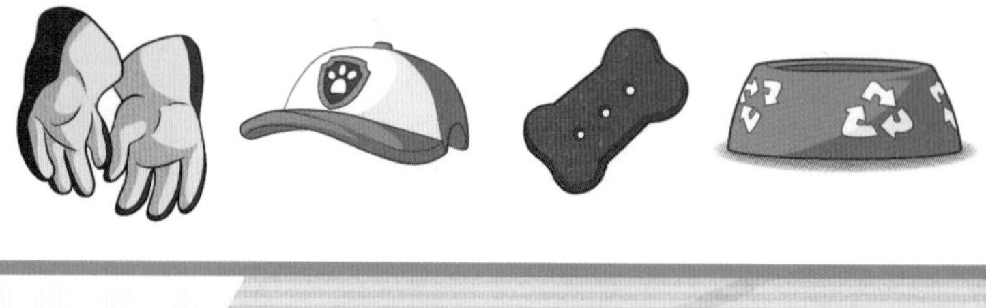

Check your answers on page 69.

44

Sand and seek

Rubble is helping out with a sandcastle competition on the beach, but he's got a bit carried away. Look at all the sandcastles he's made!

Check your answers on page 69.

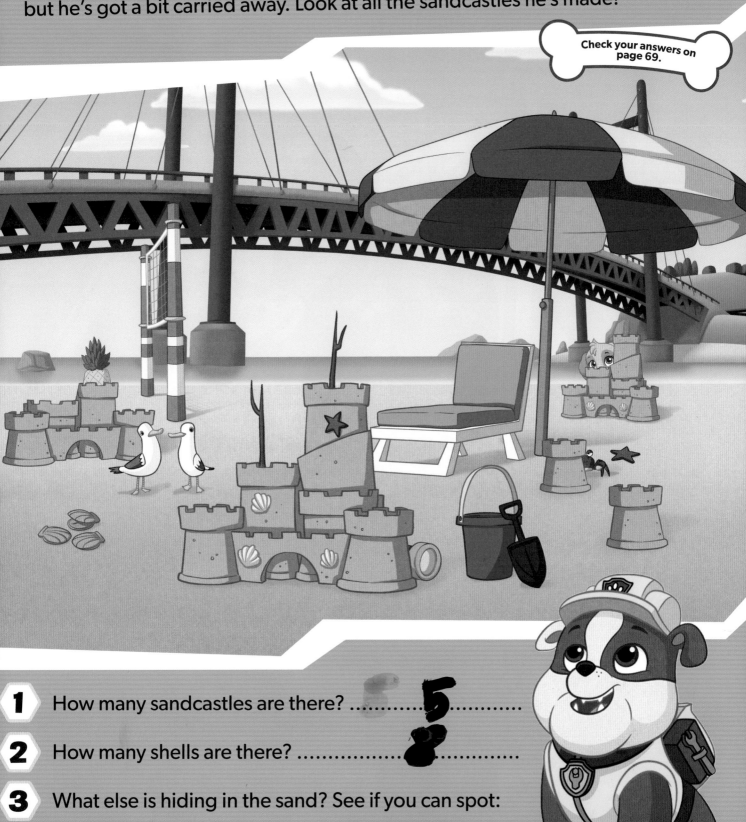

1 How many sandcastles are there? ....5............

2 How many shells are there? ....8...............

3 What else is hiding in the sand? See if you can spot:

45

Pup park playtime

Let's bark for the park! These pictures may look the same, but there are six differences in the picture on the right. Can you find them all?

A

Colour in a bone for each difference that you find.

Check your answers on page 69.

Off-duty pups

When they're not working, the PAW Patrol pups love to enjoy some ruff and tumble in the fresh air! Do you like playing outside? Here are some great games to try with your pals.

Frisbee Fun

Flying disks are brilliant fun. Grab two pals and play 'Pup in the Middle'. Two players stand apart while the third player stands in the middle and tries to grab the disk as it flies overhead.

Skye Skip

Skye loves to fly and this game keeps your feet off the ground! You need a long skipping rope, two people to turn the rope and one to skip. Take it in turns to jump high over the turning rope.

Football Crazy

Football is a great game! Put one person in goal while the other tries to score. Then practise passing between players or work on your ball skills. See how long you can keep the ball in the air using your feet, knees, chest and head.

Maize maze

Mayor Goodway's pet hen Chickaletta has wandered off to look for corn. Chase and Marshall are hot on her trail! Help Chase follow his nose and lead them to the cheeky chicken.

START

FINISH

After you've rescued Chickaletta, use your crayons or pencils to colour her feathers in yellow.

Check your answer on page 69.

Ice team

The PAW Patrol were getting ready to see their friend Jake at the ice fields. There was a loud **roar** and a huge truck rolled into view.

"Presenting the PAW Patroller," shouted Ryder. "It's a Lookout on wheels. It can take us anywhere!"

The massive vehicle was big enough to fit in all of the pups and their vehicles. A side door opened and a mechanical dog trotted out.

"Robo Dog will be our driver," smiled Ryder.

Ryder was showing the pups around the PAW Patroller when Jake popped up on the PupPad screen.

"Hey Jake," asked Ryder. "How are the ice fields?"

"Amazing!" Jake declared.

Behind him, snowy hills and an icy river glittered in the sunshine.

Suddenly, poor Jake **slipped** on the ice. His backpack rolled down the slope ... straight into the water!

"My phone, my maps, all my stuff!" he yelled.

The pups yelped in surprise.

"Jake's in big trouble," cried Rubble.

"Get your vehicles," urged Ryder.

Robo Dog started the PAW Patroller's engine, and then opened the back door so everyone could hop on board.

Jake was in danger. He tried to fish his backpack out of the river, but ended up slipping further down the riverbank towards the freezing water. Just as he was about to **plunge** in headfirst, a husky pup appeared and dragged him to safety.

"Sweet save," said Jake. The pup wagged her tail, and then introduced herself.

"My name's Everest," she exclaimed. "I've always wanted to do a real rescue!"

Everest told Jake that a storm was blowing in. She invited him to shelter in her igloo.

"I wouldn't want to lose my first rescue in a blizzard," she said cheerfully.

"How are we going to get to the igloo?" wondered Jake.

"We can do this ..." said Everest, flopping down onto her tummy and pushing off down the slope with her back paws.

Jake slid after the pup. A group of playful penguins joined in, too.

"Belly-bogganing!" Jake laughed.

The new friends **whizzed** faster and faster down the hill.

By the time the PAW Patrol reached the ice fields, it was snowing hard. The team quickly found Jake's phone and backpack, but there was no sign of him at all. Just then, Ryder noticed something on the ground.

"Are those tracks?" he asked.

"That's Jake all right," Chase nodded, sniffing the footprints. "And he's got another pup with him!"

"Let's follow them," said Ryder.

Chase followed the tracks through the snow, while Skye took to the frosty air in her helicopter.

"This pup's got to fly!" she cried.

Just at that moment, Everest and Jake had reached a narrow bridge made of ice. It stretched across a deep, dark ravine.

"My igloo is just across there," Everest said.

Jake looked worried.

"Will the ice hold our weight?" he asked.

But Jake had no choice. The ice bridge was the only way to the igloo.

"Follow me," said Everest.

Jake and Everest were only halfway across the bridge when the ice **cracked**. Suddenly it collapsed beneath them!

Skye hovered overhead at just the right time. She **swooped** in, catching Jake and Everest with a rope. But just as she was swinging them to the other side of the ravine, the rope snapped.

Everest leaped to safety, but poor Jake was left holding on to the edge. If his grasp slipped he would fall. He needed help ... and fast!

"I've got you!" called Everest.
The plucky pup grabbed hold of Jake's sleeve with her teeth, then slowly pulled him back onto the cliff top. He was safe at last.
"Yes!" cheered Jake. "Two rescues in one day!"

That night, everyone sat toasting marshmallows around the fire outside Jake's cabin. Jake smiled at his new friend, Everest.

"I could use a smart pup like you to help out on the mountain," he said. "Would you come and work with me?"

Everest **beamed** with pride.

"And for showing such great rescue skills," chipped in Ryder. "I'd like to make you an official member of the PAW Patrol."

The pups gave a happy **cheer**.

"This is the best day ever!" barked Everest.

THE END

Ice to meet you

Everest is the brilliant new member of the PAW Patrol team! She zooms up and down mountains in her Snowcat, working as a Forest Ranger.

1 Here's Everest with her fellow PAW Patrol buddy, Skye. Draw lines to match the missing puzzle pieces to the shapes in the picture.

A   **B**   **C**

2 Chase and Marshall are learning about Everest's wild and snowy habitat. Draw a line to match each word to the correct fact.

A. When water freezes it turns to .... ~~ice~~

B. A house made of snow is called an .... ~~igloo~~

C. Everest and Jake live high up in the .... ~~mountains~~

D. Everest drives a .... mobile. ~~snow~~

snow

ice

mountains

igloo

3 Everest is having a belly-bogganing race down the mountain with Skye, Zuma and Rubble. Trace the trails with your finger to find out who will reach the finish line first, and then circle the winning pup!

Check your answers on page 69.

FINISH LINE

Duck delivery

Chase has called for back up – these ducks need to be returned to their pond! Rubble is rushing to the rescue with his digger to give them a ride home. Complete the dot-to-dot, and then colour in the picture.

Va-va-vroom!

The PAW Patrol is equipped for emergencies on land, in the sea or in the air. Look at the pictures, choose a scene and then design the perfect rescue vehicle to match.

Will it have handlebars or a steering wheel?

Will your vehicle have wheels, skis or tracks?

Pups at play

Are you ready for some arty fun? Challenge a pup-loving pal to this PAWsome colouring game!

YOU WILL NEED:

- Two players
- One dice
- Crayons or colouring pencils in dark and light brown, grey, black, blue, yellow, green, orange and pink.

WHAT TO DO:

1 Sit with the book turned round so that the picture of Chase is in front of player one and Rocky is in front of player two.

2 Take it in turns to roll the dice. The player with the highest number should go first.

3 Each time you roll the dice, check the **DICE KEY** below and colour in the part of the pup that matches the number of spots on the dice.

4 Take it in turns to throw the dice and colour the pictures. The winner is the first player to have a fully coloured pup.

DICE KEY

1 spot	colour the face
2 spots	colour an ear
3 spots	colour the body
4 spots	colour the tail
5 spots	colour the collar and tag
6 spots	colour two legs and paws

If you throw a number, but you have already coloured that part, pass the dice on and miss a turn.

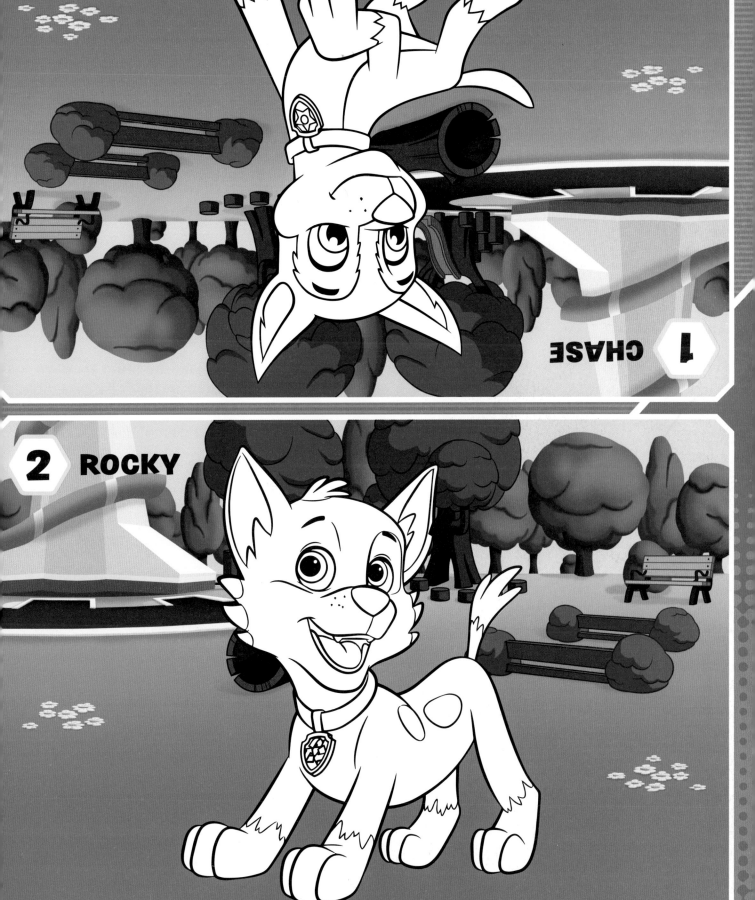

1 CHASE

2 ROCKY

Canine card

It's important to thank someone who has been kind, thoughtful or helpful. This great card is the paw-fect way to say it!

YOU WILL NEED:

- A sheet of A4 thin white card
- A square of brown paper
- Coloured crayons, pens or pencils
- Glue
- Scissors
- The pictures on the yellow background, on the opposite page.

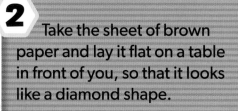

1 Fold the card in half, as shown above.

2 Take the sheet of brown paper and lay it flat on a table in front of you, so that it looks like a diamond shape.

3 Bring the top corner down to meet the bottom corner, making a triangle shape.

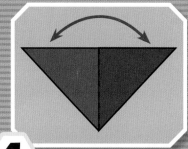

4 Fold the side corners together, and then unfold the paper again.

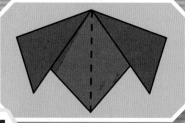

5 To make the pup's ears, fold the corners down and towards you, using the top of the fold line as a guide.

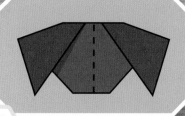

6 Now fold the top and bottom of the paper away from you, so that the head and chin are no longer pointy.

64

! Make sure that you finish the activity on page 66 before you cut out sections from this page! !

Your pup is finished! Bring him or her to life by drawing their eyes, nose, mouth and tongue.

Glue the folds at the back of the pup's head and chin to the front of the card.

Yelp for help! Scissors are sharp. Ask a grown-up to make this card with you.

Open your card up and write a PAW Patrol message inside. You could copy or cut out the words and pictures below.

© Spin Master

Thank you!

You're PAWfect

You're the best!

You rock!

You are totally PAWsome!

Chase thinks you're ace!

Teamwork trio

Hooray for teamwork! The PAW Patrol pups know working together is the best way to get any job done.

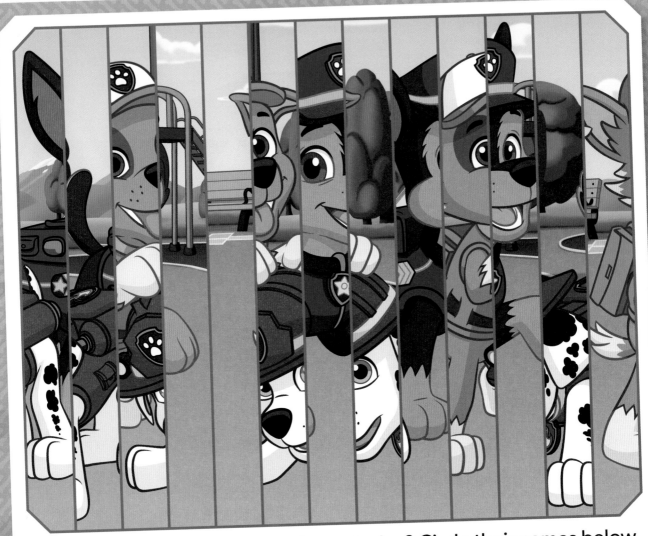

Which three pups have joined forces today? Circle their names below.

Rubble

Everest

Marshall

Rocky

Chase

Skye

Zuma

Check your answers on page 69.

All paws on deck

Have you lent a paw today? Fill in this cool PAW Patrol certificate, and then ask a grown-up to put it on display.

CONGRATULATIONS!

....
Write your name here.

has lent a paw and helped with

....

Good work!
Three cheers for you!

Answers

Page 9

Page 11

1. Marshall is spotty

3.

START

FINISH

Page 13

1.

3. Rubble has 7 bones.

Page 15

1.

3.

Page 17

1.

3. It's a star.

Page 19

1. B

Page 21

1.

3. A. Yes.
   B. No. She drives a snowmobile called a SnowCat.
   C. No. She lives with Jake in the mountains.

Page 22

1. Everest
2. Zuma
3. Skye
4. Marshall
5. Rubble
6. Rocky

Page 23

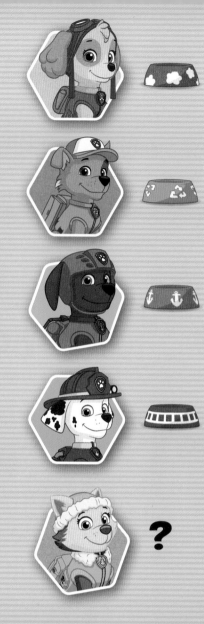

Everest's bowl is missing.

Pages 24-25

1. Chase
2. Pink
3. Marshall
4. A bone
5. Everest is next to Chase
6. No

Page 34

1–D, 2–B, 3–A, 4–C

Page 35

Calling **Ryder**,
It's **Skye**. This is an S.O.S. Call the PAW Patrol on your **PupPad**! I was out in my

elicopter when I saw a
ot air balloon caught on
e bridge. I could see that
omeone was trapped in the
asket of the balloon.
lease ask **Chase** to stop the
affic going over the bridge
o that **Marshall** can get them
own with his ladder. **Zuma**
hould wait in the water
nder the bridge, just in case.
AW Patrol, let's roll!

ages 38-39
. hovercraft

age 40
–D, 2–B, 3–C, 4–E, 5–A

age 44

age 45
here are 5 sandcastles.
here are 8 shells.

Pages 46-47

Page 49

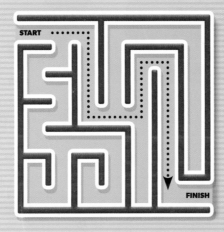

Pages 58–59
1.

2.
A. ice
B. igloo
C. mountains
D. snow

3.

Page 66

Rocky   Chase

Marshall